LOOK LIVE
REST EAST

Stories, songs, tricks and rhymes to rouse and to relax

chosen by Helen East
With illustrations by Jane Ray

A & C BLACK · LONDON

LOOK LIVELY

Good morning ①

Greeting song from Sierra Leone, arranged and sung by Folo Graff

Good morning, good morning,
**   good morning to you all,**
We've just come to ask you
**   about a Christmas morning.**

This is a Christmas good morning song from Sierra Leone. You can use it for any day of the week or special occasion. As you can hear on the cassette, Folo sings about Christmas and New Year. In the last verse, he sings, 'I've just come to ask you ow unah all do-o?' which is pidgin for 'how everybody's doing?'

Make up your own verses by changing the last two lines, e.g.

We've just come to wish you
    a happy Monday morning.
We've just come to wish Jake
    a happy birthday morning.

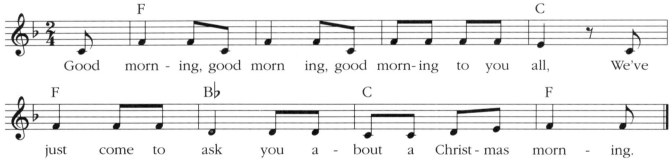

Rise at 6 ②

English rhyme

Rise at 6
Dine at 10
Sup at 6
Sleep at 10
You will live to 10 x 10

Did you sleep well? ③

Bohemian saying

If someone asks, 'Did you sleep well?'
Answer in a roundabout way.
If you answer them directly
They can take your sleep away.

Snore snore snore ④

Cumulative sound story by Helen East

A little old lady fell into a doze,
    Snore, snore, snore,
With the fire a-warming her gnarly old toes,
    Snore, snore, snore,
She dozed all night and she dozed all day,
    Snore, snore, snore,
She dozed the daylight half away,
    Snore, snore, snore.

The budgie was thirsty and started to squark,
    Snore, snore, snore,
    Squark!
The dog was a-barking to go for a walk,
    Snore, snore, snore,
    Squark!
    Woof–woof!
The donkey was braying, the cat
    caterwauling,
    Snore, snore, snore,
    Squark!
    Woof!–woof!
    Hee–haw, meeowwwwwl!
But still the old lady went on with her
    snoring,
    Snore, snore, snore.

Her daughter came round for some tea and a
    chat,
    Snore, snore, snore,
    Squark!
    Woof!–woof!
    Hee–haw, meeowwwwwl!
    Chat–chat, chat–chat, chat–chat,
She rang on the doorbell and rattled the latch,
    Snore, snore, snore,
    Squark!
    Woof–woof!
    Hee–haw, meeowwwwwl!
    Chat–chat, chat–chat, chat–chat,
    Brrrring, brrrring, brattle!

She called all the neighbours to bang on the
    door,
    Snore, snore, snore,
    Squark!
    Woof–woof!
    Hee–haw, meeowwwwwl!
    Chat–chat, chat–chat, chat–chat,
    Brrrring, brrrring, brattle!
    Bang bang, bang bang, bang bang.
But still the old lady did nothing but snore,
    Snore, snore, snore.

Then out popped a mouse from his hole by the
    door,
    Snore, snore, snore . . . *(etc)*
Says he, 'I can't stand this uproar any more.'
    Snore, snore, snore . . . *(etc)*
He scrambled up onto the old lady's head,
    Snore, snore, snore . . . *(etc)*
Grabbed hold of her nose – and the snoring
    stopped dead. _____

And when they heard that, all the people
    outside,
    Chat–chat, chat–chat, chat–chat,
    Brrrring, brrrring, bratttle!
    Bang bang, bang bang, bang bang.
And the dog and the donkey, the cat and the
    bird,
    Squark!
    Woof–woof!
    Hee–haw, meeowwwwwl!
STOPPED _____
And listened instead to a silence so deep,
It startled the old lady out of her sleep.

Everyone can take a part in acting this one out. Choose someone to be the old lady, someone else to be the budgie, and so on. Have a whole crowd of neighbours. Use your voices and find instruments for the noises, which should all be made at the same time, not one after the other.

Nu wahtan ⑤

Waking song from the Gambia, sung by Marie Ngum

Lai lah lah lah eh lah lah,
      neneh na nu wahtan,
Lai lah lah lah eh lah lah,
      neneh na nu wahtan.

Anna* suma neneh boye
      woye nah lah na nu wahtan.
Lai lah lah lah eh lah lah . . .

Yow dai urus si ngalam nga
      woye nah lah na nu wahtan.
Lai lah lah lah eh lah lah . . .

Lai lah lah lah eh lah lah,
      neneh na nu wahtan.

Mothers in the Gambia like their babies to wake up gently. As the child wakes, they sing this soothing song for five to ten minutes. It means:

Let's get talking baby,
Wake up Anna, baby sweet.
Leave your sleep and talk to me,
You are like gold dust to me.

* substitute child's name

Lai lah lah lah eh lah lah, ne-neh na nu wah-tan.——

An-na su-ma ne-neh bo-ye woye nah lah na nu wah-tan.——

Lai lah lah lah eh lah lah, ne-neh na nu wah-tan.——

Yow dai urus sin-ga-lam nga—— woye nah lah nah nu wah-tan.——

Waking the Mogul princess ⑥

True story from India, retold by Nikhat Mohamed

There was a Mogul princess who had to be woken each morning so gently, so very gently. Her maid would bring her a rose bud, and stroke her with it on her feet saying, 'Wake up, Princess, even the rose bud wants to see you so much that she rubs your feet with her eyes.'

And then, when the princess opened her eyes, she liked to see a lucky face. If she had bad luck, she blamed the person whom she first saw on waking up. So what did her maids do? They brought her a mirror, so the first face she saw was her own!

Bad luck! (7)

English/Jamaican rap by Helen East and Carol Sherman

Who who who got up wrong this morning?
Who turned left, forgot about yawning?
Who put a sock on inside out?
Who made it worse by putting it right?
Who crossed paths with a person on the stairs?
Who tumbled at the door? Who saw a hare?
Who sang before them nyam? Who didn't eat?
Who put the right shoes on the wrong feet?
Me say who who who.
Me tink say you you you.

If you did that you'd have terrible bad luck unless you took off your right shoe and ran out the door. Then someone would have to throw your shoe out after you. That would give you a second chance – a new start.

Dr Knickerbocker (8)

Rhythm game collected in England

During the first two lines, everyone dances round the leader in the middle. Then the leader makes up a rhythm for each part of the body, and the others have to copy:

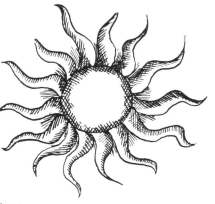

Dr Knickerbocker, number forty-nine
Sure gets drunk on a bottle of wine.

Leader: **Now I got the rhythm in my head – tap tap tap**

Answer: ***Now we got the rhythm in our heads – tap tap tap***

Leader: **Now I got the rhythm in my eyes –** *(roll eyes)*

Answer: ***Now we got the rhythm in our eyes –*** *(roll eyes)*

Leader: **Now I got the rhythm in my hands – clap clap clap clap clap**

Answer: ***Now we got the rhythm in our hands – clap clap clap clap clap***

Leader: **Now I got the rhythm in my hips – ooh la la** *(sway hips)*

Answer: ***Now we got the rhythm in our hips – ooh la la*** *(sway hips)*

Leader: **Now I got the rhythm in my knees – slap**

Answer: ***Now we got the rhythm in our knees – slap***

Leader: **Now I got the rhythm in my feet – stamp stamp stamp**

Answer: ***Now we got the rhythm in our feet – stamp stamp stamp***

Leader: **Now count up to nine –**

Everyone: **One, two, three, four, five, six, seven, eight, NINE!**

Count round the circle. Number nine becomes the next leader.

Why the nightingale sings better than the dove ⑨

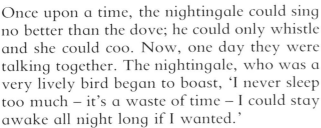

Romanian story, retold by Rick Wilson and Helen East

Once upon a time, the nightingale could sing no better than the dove; he could only whistle and she could coo. Now, one day they were talking together. The nightingale, who was a very lively bird began to boast, 'I never sleep too much – it's a waste of time – I could stay awake all night long if I wanted.'

'Nonsense – nobody can keep away sleep if sleep wants to close his eyes,' said the dove, who was a very placid, sleep-loving bird.

'You are wrong,' protested the nightingale. 'Anyway, let's see who is right. You know the one song I can sing, and I know yours. Let us keep awake tonight and learn some new tunes. You'll soon see – it's easy to stay wide awake if you look lively and listen.'

So they made a bet on it, and that night they perched on different trees in the same meadow, ready to stay awake as long as they could.

The nightingale listened to the sounds borne on the night air. Over the fields came the melancholy bark of a dog. ____ He listened and he copied.

The wind whispered and sighed a lullaby. ____ The nightingale tried that. A shepherd played his pipe away in his hut on the hillside ____ and the nightingale echoed. The bleating of newborn lambs, ____ the ripple of the river, ____ and the twitter of a sleepy bird ____ the nightingale copied them all.

All night long he stayed awake listening, and the time flew by. Each new tune he learnt he practised and practised and then softly, under his breath, he wove them all together into a wonderful new song.

Now, when the dove heard the wind's lullaby, it lulled her to sleep almost at once and she slept the whole night through until, at last, dawn came. As she woke up, she listened and heard the farmer getting out his team of horses and chirruping to them as he drove them to the uplands.

'Chirrup, chirrup, trr, trr,' he called, and this the dove remembered.

When the sun was up, the nightingale flew across to her. 'Well,' he said, 'I have had a wonderful night. I've learnt lots of new tunes – just listen to this.

The dove was very humble. She confessed that sleep had overcome her and that she had only learnt one little note.

So 'coo coo' she still sings to herself all day long – but just sometimes she sings, 'trr trr,' when she remembers the farmer calling to his horses.

As for the nightingale, he was happy. And if *you* look lively and stay awake long enough, you will hear him and then you'll be happy too. For the nightingale now has the most glorious song of all – all because, once upon a time, he looked lively and listened.

You can hear a real nightingale singing on the cassette. During the story you will hear some extracts from Romanian folk tunes which sound like the nightingale learning his new songs. Can you whistle them?

El calentamiento (10)

Mexican song arranged and sung by Héo Legorreta

The rider (jinete) is playing a limbering up game. See if you can join in. As soon as a part of the body is mentioned start moving it – shake it, wave it, flex those muscles! Keep moving until the call Jinete! A la carga! Freeze – then begin again.

Este el juego del calentamiento,
Habra que ver la carga del jinete.
  Jinete! A la carga! Una mano!
    (wave or shake one hand in the air)

Este el juego del calentamiento,
Habra que ver la carga del jinete,
  Jinete! A la carga! Una mano,
            la otra.
    (wave or shake both hands in the air)

Continue the song in the same way, adding another part of the body each time:
un brazo *(one arm)*
el otro *(the other)*
los hombros *(the shoulders)*
la cadera *(the hips)*
un pie *(one foot)*
el otro *(the other foot)*
una pierna *(one leg)*
la otra *(the other leg)*
todo el cargamento *(the whole body)*

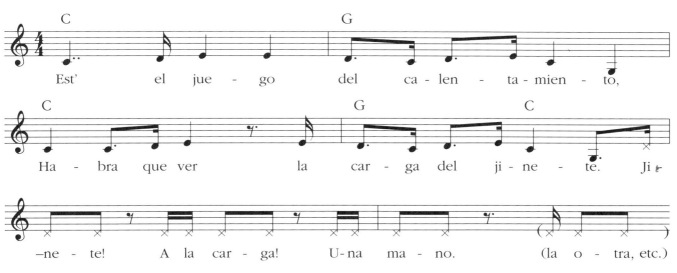

Est' el jue - go del ca - len - ta - mien - to,

Ha - bra que ver la car - ga del ji - ne - te. Ji

-ne - te! A la car - ga! U-na ma - no. (la o - tra, etc.)

De bwoy Jack nimble (11)

English/Jamaican rhyme told by Connie Mark

De bwoy Jack nimble, de bwoy Jack quick,
De bwoy Jack jump over candalstick.
Jump! jump! jump!

Take turns to do the jumping, and put your own name in instead of Jack. Change jump to hop, skip, dance, or whatever you like.

Riddle me red or guess me grey,
Show me who's jag or sajag today.

The golden bridge (12)

London street riddle, retold by Helen East

Imagine you're asleep and you are dreaming that you are lying on a grassy bank, and all around you are flowers and trees blossoming. Mmmm, they smell delicious. And there are birds singing and the sun is shining; it's a beautiful day. And just beside you is a river, flowing along gently. So you stand up and you begin to walk along beside the river and you walk and you walk until you come to a bend in the river, and there, spanning the river is a bridge that is made of solid gold.

Now you've never stepped onto gold before, so you take your shoes and socks off and you walk across that bridge. And you can feel the gold, cold against your toes. And you walk and walk; you go over the hump in the middle of the bridge. You are just coming to the other side, just coming towards the bank of the river, when all of a sudden – GRRRR!

There in front of you is a huge sabretooth tiger! Now you thought sabretoothed tigers were extinct and so did I, but they obviously aren't, because there is one, and it's looking very hungry! So – keeping your eyes fixed on that tiger, you begin to back away slowly, back over the hump of the bridge, back towards the safety of the other side. But before you get to the other side, suddenly you hear SSSSSSS!

And there, behind you, blocking your exit is a huge king cobra with its hood up ready to strike. So now, you've got a tiger in front, a cobra behind. The obvious thing is to jump into the water. But just as you are about to jump in the water you look down and what do you see? – the smiling mouths of a hundred crocodiles waiting.

Cobra behind, tiger in front, crocodiles below. What will you do? Think quick! An easy way out is simply to . . .

A mosquito one (13)

Counting game from Guyana, called by
Doris Harper-Wills

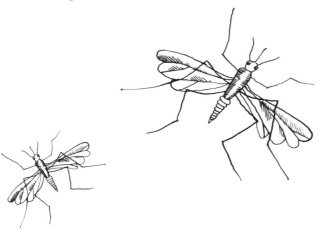

This is a counting game – slap the floor or clap on the beat ★ and hold up the correct number of fingers as you call out the numbers. Make up actions for lines 2, 4, 6, 8 and 10.

A mosquito one, a mosquito two,
A mosquito jump in the old man shoe,
A mosquito three, a mosquito four,
A mosquito open the old man door.
A mosquito five, a mosquito six,
A mosquito pick up the old man sticks.
A mosquito seven, a mosquito eight,
A mosquito open the old man gate,
A mosquito nine, a mosquito ten,
A mosquito biting the man again.

Skunny Wundy's skipping stone

Native American Seneca story, retold by Joseph Bruchac

Long ago, in a little village by the Otsiningo River, there lived a boy named Skunny-Wundy. He was not as big or as strong as the other boys, but he could do two things better than the others – think fast and skip stones. Though the other boys tried, none beat him at stone skipping. Sometimes they'd ask Skunny-Wundy to join them throwing stones at frogs and turtles on the river bank. Skunny-Wundy would never do that. His mother had told him stories about the animals and he didn't want to hurt them. Finally, none of the other boys would skip stones with him, but Skunny-Wundy didn't mind. Almost any day he could be found by the river, skipping stones. Skunny-Wundy always went to the south because of what his parents told him.

'Why must I never go to the north?' Skunny-Wundy asked.

'Listen,' his mother said. 'To the north there are terrible beings, giants whose skins are made of stone. Arrows and spears bounce off them. They are taller than pine trees! And do you know what they like to eat?'

Skunny-Wundy shook his head, though he knew the answer. He'd heard such stories from his parents before.

'People!' said Skunny-Wundy's father. 'A boy like you would be one bite for a stone giant. But if they don't see people, they forget we exist. If they weren't so stupid they would have wiped out all the people long ago. So do not go to the north.'

For a long time, or so it seemed to Skunny-Wundy, he did as his parents said. Whenever he skipped stones on the river he went south. When he returned he never went past his own village. But it grew harder and harder to find good skipping stones.

One day Skunny-Wundy rose very early, before the sun. No one else was awake. He said to himself, 'It won't matter if I walk just a *little* ways towards the north. I won't go far.'

As soon as he started north he found a good skipping stone. Another one, though, further on, was better! Gradually, he went around the bend in the river, leaving the village far behind. Finally, as the sun reached the middle of the sky, he found a stone that was perfect. It was just the right weight, smooth and flat. Setting his feet, he cocked his arm and threw. It skipped twelve times before it sank, leaving a row of rings on the river's smooth surface.

'WEH-YOH!' Skunny-Wundy shouted. 'I am the best skipper of stones in the world!'

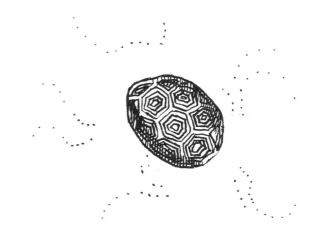

'HAH-A-AH,' roared a great voice over his head, so loud it shook the ground under his feet. 'You are not the greatest skipper of stones!'

Skunny-Wundy looked up. There, looming over the trees, was the biggest, hungriest-looking stone giant anyone could imagine. It reached down, picked up a flat stone as big as a bear and threw it across the river. That stone skipped fifteen times before it sank!

'HAH-A-AH,' the stone giant roared again. 'You see who is the greatest skipper of stones. Now I am going to eat you.'

Skunny-Wundy knew it would be no good to run. The stone giant would catch him in one stride. But he could use his wits.

'Hunh!' Skunny-Wundy said. 'Are you afraid I will beat you?'

'ENHH?' said the stone giant. 'I am afraid of no one.' He stomped his foot on the ground so hard it almost knocked Skunny-Wundy off his feet.

'If you are not afraid,' Skunny-Wundy said, 'we will have a contest to see who's better at skipping stones.'

Skunny-Wundy contd.

'Nyoh!' the stone giant said. 'I agree. Go ahead. Throw your stone. Try to beat me.'

'Ah,' Skunny-Wundy said, 'my arm is too tired now. I've been skipping stones all day. Let me go home and rest. I promise I'll come back tomorrow for our contest.'

'Nyoh,' the stone giant said. 'That is good. Tomorrow when the sun is at the top of the sky we will skip stones. If I win, then I will eat you. If you win, then maybe I will not eat you.'

'I agree,' said Skunny-Wundy, walking backwards as he spoke. 'I will return tomorrow.'

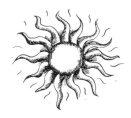

Skunny-Wundy walked very slowly until he was around the bend in the river and the stone giant could no longer see him. Then he ran as fast as he could. He didn't stop until he was within sight of his village. He sat down on a log and began to laugh. It had been so easy to outwit the stone giant. It was as his father told him. Stone giants were stupid. Then Skunny-Wundy remembered. He'd given his word he would return the next day! His parents had always told him breaking a promise was a terrible thing. Not only that, if he didn't keep his word, the stone giant might come looking for him. It only had to follow the river. It wouldn't just find Skunny-Wundy, but his whole village. It wouldn't just eat him, it would eat everyone.

When Skunny-Wundy went to bed that night he was very quiet. His mother asked if anything was wrong, but Skunny-Wundy said nothing. If he told his parents, they'd try to fight the monster. It would eat them too. The next morning, before sunrise, Skunny-Wundy walked slowly towards the north along the river, certain that this would be his last day. As he walked, though, he kept looking down. Perhaps if he found just the right stone he'd be able to beat the stone giant. He kept picking up stones and dropping them. None were just right. Then he heard a little voice from the ground ahead of him. It was calling his name!

'Skunny-Wundy, Skunny-Wundy. Take me, Skunny-Wundy. Take me, take me, take me.'

Skunny-Wundy looked down among the flat stones. Was one of them talking to him? Then he saw that what he thought to be a stone was a little turtle, its head sticking out of its shell.

'Skunny-Wundy,' the turtle said again, 'take me, take me, take me, take me.'

'You want me to use you as a skipping stone?'

'Nyoh, nyoh, nyoh, nyoh!' said the little turtle. 'We can win, we can win, we can win, we can win!'

'All right,' Skunny-Wundy said. 'A small friend is better than no friend at all when you're in trouble.'

The little turtle pulled in its head and legs. It looked just like a skipping stone. Then Skunny-Wundy placed the turtle into his belt pouch and continued on. The sun was high in the sky now. Soon he would reach the place where he was to meet the stone giant. He could hear a sound like thunder rolling and lightning striking. Skunny-Wundy peeked around a bend in the river. There stood the stone giant, holding a huge bolder. 'Hhrruummm,' the stone giant rumbled, making a sound like thunder. Then it hurled the stone. The stone skipped sixteen times and hit the other side with a sound like lightning. CRACK! Skunny-Wundy thought about running away, but he remembered his promise. He stepped around the bend.

'KWEH!' rumbled the stone giant as it saw him. 'Little food, I have been waiting for you. Are you ready to be eaten?'

Skunny-Wundy held up his hand. 'Wait!' he said. 'First we must have our contest. Remember?'

'HAH-A-AH!' the stone giant laughed. 'Throw your stone. Then I shall beat you and then I shall eat you.'

'No,' Skunny-Wundy said, 'you must go first. You challenged me.'

'NYOH,' the stone giant said. 'That is good.' It picked up a stone large as a lodge and then, 'HHRRUMMM,' hurled it. It struck the water with a great WHAP! each time it skipped. It skipped seventeen times and knocked down a dozen trees on the other side.

'Now, little food,' the stone giant said, reaching for Skunny-Wundy.

'First I must throw my stone,' Skunny-Wundy said, his voice was calm, but his heart was beating so fast he thought it would burst. He reached into his pouch for a stone and found the little turtle. He pulled it out, drew back his arm, and threw! The turtle struck the water just right and started to skip. One, two, three, four, five, six, seven times it skipped. Eight, nine, ten, eleven, twelve times. But it was slowing down. Just then, the little turtle stuck out its legs and began kicking. Thirteen, fourteen, fifteen times it skipped. Sixteen, seventeen, eighteen, nineteen, twenty times and now it was skipping in circles. Twenty-one, twenty-two, twenty-three, twenty-four

times it skipped and then sank beneath the surface.

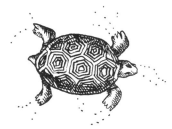

'WEH-YOH!' Skunny-Wundy shouted. 'I have won. Eat me if you want, but you have lost!'

The stone giant became very angry. It had never been defeated at anything before. It started to shake with rage. It shook and shook. It shook so hard cracks appeared in its body. Flakes of rock flecked from its cheeks. Harder and harder it shook until it collapsed into a pile of little stones.

So it was that with the help of this friend, the little turtle, Skunny-Wundy defeated his first stone giant.

Dummy dance ⑮

Australian aboriginal dance, contributed by Rick Wilson

This is a sitting down dance – easy to do, but a lot more exhausting than it sounds. Sit crosslegged and bounce your knees on the beat (X) as high as you can throughout the whole dance. There are four beats played on the bamboo log to count you in. On the big X, clap. On the little x, pat your knees. Shout HA! and fling your arms to the left. Shout HE! and fling your arms forwards. Shout HO! and fling your arms to the right.

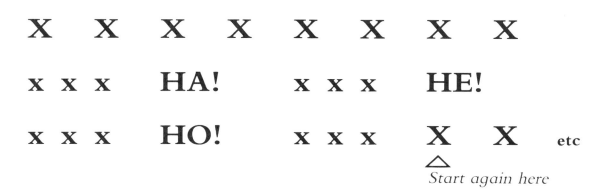

Easy? That's the whole dance, but it repeats as many times as you can do it, always starting with the eight handclaps. Each time round, make the handclaps faster – remember, your knees have to bounce faster too . . . Try it with the tape.

A Highland lullaby 🔟6

Scottish song, sung by Andy Haveron

I left my baby lying there,
   lying there, lying there,
I left my baby lying there,
   to go and gather blaeberries.

Hovan hovan gorry og o,
   Gorry og o, gorry og o,
Hovan hovan gorry og o,
   I never found my baby-o.

I found a wee brown otter's trail,
   otter's trail, otter's trail,
I found a wee brown otter's trail,
   but never found my baby-o,

Hovan hovan gorry og o . . .

I heard the curlew crying high,
   crying high, crying high,
I heard the curlew crying high,
   but never heard my baby-o.

Hovan hovan gorry og o . . .

The King's storyteller 🄗

Retold by Duncan Williamson

A long time ago, there once lived a King and a Queen in a kingdom (anywhere – we don't know where it existed – it could have been Scotland or anywhere in the east). The happiness of the King and Queen's life was their baby son, it was their very first baby son and the Queen loved him dearly.

In these bygone times, queens always had ladies-in-waiting, maids and nannies to care for children, but this particular Queen would let no one touch her baby son. She would take care of him by herself and after the evening meal was over and everything was finished for the evening in the palace, the enjoyment of the Queen was to take her baby son on her knee and tell him all these wonderful stories – stories she'd heard from her grandmother. And the baby son would lie on his mother's knee and he'd fall asleep and she'd carry him off and put him to his bed quietly and then go and leave him in peace to sleep the whole night over. Nothing would make the Queen happier than telling him stories. So the years passed by and when their son was four years old, she was still telling him stories.

Then there was a terrible tragedy in the kingdom. The King was out hunting with his huntsmen after wild boar and he fell from his horse and was killed. The Queen was so upset – it nearly broke her heart to be left without her husband the King. But she thought to herself, 'I must continue for the sake of my baby son, because some day he will be King when I am gone to meet my husband.'

So she continued to tell him all those wonderful stories, and the years passed by with sadness in her heart until one evening, when the little Prince was ten years old, she thought that the time had come to talk to him.

She called him into her little chamber, where she spent most of her time and said, 'My son, I'd like to talk to you.'

'Yes mummy, what do you want to talk about?'

'My son – someday I must leave you because some day I'll get old. Some day, you'll be King!'

'Me, be King? Will I be rich when I'm King?'

'Of course, my son, you'll be rich.'

'Can I have anything I want when I become King?'

'Yes, my son, you can have anything your heart desires when you become King. Is there anything I've never given you?'

'No, not really, but you tell me that some day you'll be gone to join my father, who I don't remember much about, and I'll be left alone – who will tell me stories when you're gone? Even though I'll be the King, I'll need someone to tell me stories.'

'Oh my son, if that's your only problem – there are many storytellers in your kingdom who will tell you stories.'

'Well, when I become King, I will find a storyteller and if you say I will become rich, I will make *him* rich – I'll give him a large reward and he will become my storyteller. And he will tell me stories just like you. Of course I'll be sad, but I'll also have a storyteller.'

So the little Prince was happy and the years passed by and he grew up to become a young man, and when he was twenty years old, his mother died. There was sorrow in the land when the old Queen died but after time passed by, the young Prince was crowned King. And the very first thing he did – he sent couriers and riders all over the land telling all the storytellers to come before him because he wanted

The King's storyteller contd.

someone to tell him stories. He would give them a large reward but they must be able to tell a story the way his mother did.

So storytellers came from far and near and they sat before the King and they told wonderful stories that they'd heard. And the King sat there in the evenings and he listened to every storyteller and when the story had ended, he would turn to the storyteller and say, 'That was a wonderful story you told me, but not the way my mother told me . . .'

'Alas,' cried the King at last, 'Is there no one in my kingdom who can tell me a story the way my mother did?'

'But in the King's palace gardens, there lived a little gardener. He was very poor, very small and very old and he worked for a few pennies in the King's garden. And he too watched the storytellers come and go from the palace, thinking to himself, 'I wonder – has the king found a storyteller?' Because he knew how important a storyteller was to the King – because the story had spread far and wide across the land. And he thought to himself, 'Whoever becomes the King's storyteller will become very rich, receive a large reward and never need to work in the palace garden like me for a few pence. Oh, I wish I could be a storyteller,' thought the little gardener. But then he thought to himself, 'Why not! Maybe I could become a storyteller, because I remember all those stories my mother told me when I was small. Maybe I could tell the King a story.'

So then he made up his mind. That very evening, he would go before the King and tell him a story. So he tidied himself up, washed his face, put on the best clothes he could afford and appeared before the King at the palace. And the guards cried, 'Another storyteller for the King – welcome!'

So the little gardener was led before the King, who sat in his chair in his chamber and, to his amazement, the King knew the little gardener. 'My little friend, you've come to tell me a story – continue then, tell me a story!'

And the gardener sat before the King and told him a wonderful story that he'd heard from his mother, and the King loved the story but then, turning to the little gardener he said, 'Your story was very good. You are good. You are a great storyteller but, you see, it was not the way my mother told me. But because you're so good, I'll give you another two chances. Come again tomorrow night and tell me another story.'

So the second evening, the little gardener came before the King and told him another beautiful story. The King listened to every word and said, 'That was a wonderful story but, not *just* the way my mother told me. But you've one more chance – come again tomorrow night.'

So, for the third evening, the little gardener came again and sat before the King and began to tell him another beautiful story. But halfway through the story, he looked and the King was sound asleep.

'Oh dear,' thought the gardener, 'what have I done? My story was so bad that it's bored the King to sleep. When he wakes up he's going to have my head for this! Oh why did I ever think I could become a storyteller? I couldn't tell the King a story like his mother. Now, when he wakes up, he's going to have my head for boring him to sleep! I must make myself away from the palace and this kingdom, where he'll never find me. I've bored him to sleep!'

The King was still asleep when the gardener quietly made himself away from the palace to his little cottage. And he sat there trembling all night long, saying to himself, 'I've bored the King to sleep – he's going to have my head. What will happen when he wakes up?'

And he sat in his house all night long, waiting for daybreak. He was going to run away where no one would find him.

But just when the sun rose in the east, down from the palace came two great big guards with their spears, marching to the little gardener's cottage. They stopped and said, 'Little gardener, the King wants to see you.'

'Oh dear,' said the gardener, 'Why did I ever think I could become a storyteller? I bored the King to sleep. Now he's going to have my head! I was happy in the garden working for a few pence. It's better than losing your head.'

But he was marched before the King and he bowed and said, 'My Lord, I'm sorry!'

But the King said, 'You're sorry, my little gardener? Why?'

'I'm sorry my story was so bad!'

'You're story was not bad,' said the King. 'It was good! And I've called you here before me to give you my reward and to be my storyteller because, you see, at last I've found someone who can tell me a story the way my mother did.'

So the little gardener became the King's storyteller and he sat all those evenings and told the King all those wonderful stories. And he never minded sometimes if the King fell asleep before the story ended because he knew in his heart, at last the King had found someone who could tell him a story the way his mother did. And what did the King's mother's stories do to him? Put him to sleep!

North south east west ⓲

Saying from Eastern Europe and Asia

Head to the south or head to the west,
That's the way to sleep the best.
Head to the east bad luck may fall,
Head to the north is worst of all.

Night night ⓳

English rhyme

Night night, sleep tight,
Hope the bugs don't bite.
If they do, take a shoe,
Beat them 'til they're black
and blue.

Juan Pestañas 20

Mexican lullaby, adapted, arranged and sung by Héo Legorreta

Buenas noches, hasta mañana,
Que Juan Pestañas ya va a venir.
Ponte tu pijama, métete a la cama,
Que ya es la hora de dormir.

Alla viene Don Juan Pestañas,
Te toca un pié y te quedas quieto.
Otro pié tocó, la espalda y las piernas
Y poco a poquito te durmió.

Alla viene Don Juan Pestañas,
Toca una mano y te quedas quieto.
La otra te tocó, los brazos y el cuello
Y poco a poquito te durmió.

Alla viene Don Juan Pestañas,
Tocó la boca y te quedas quieto,
Un ojo tocó y el otro también
Y poco a poquito te durmió,
Y poco a poquito te durmió.

Tus ojitos se van cerrando
Tranquilamente y sin despertar,
Sueñas con el mar, la luna y el sol
Y así Juan Pestañas ya se va,
Y así Juan Pestañas ya se fué.

Juan Pestañas' magic touch puts you to sleep bit by bit. Relax each part of the body as it is mentioned.

Translation

Good night, till tomorrow,
John Eyelashes (Juan Pestañas) is coming.
Put on your pyjamas, get into bed,
It's time to sleep now.

Here comes Mr John Eyelashes,
He touches one foot and you feel it go still,
He touches the other foot, your back and your
    legs,
And little by little he makes you sleep.

Here comes Mr John Eyelashes,
He touches your hand and you feel it go still,
He touches the other hand, your arms and
    your neck
And little by little he makes you sleep.

Here comes Mr John Eyelashes,
He touches your mouth and you feel it go still,
He touches one eye and the other one too,
And little by little he makes you sleep.

Your little eyes are closing gradually,
Peacefully, and without waking up,
You dream with the sea, the moon and the
    sun,
And so John Eyelashes is going,
And so John Eyelashes is gone.

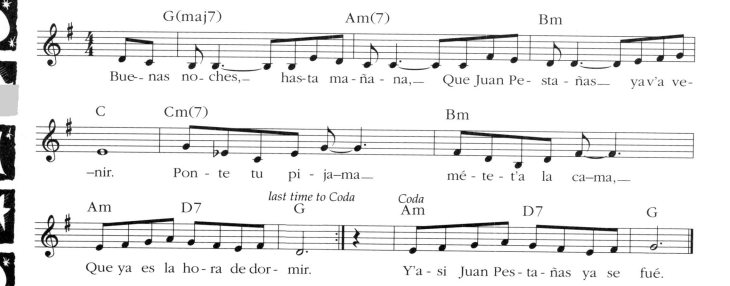

The sleep thief 21

Saying from Germany

A witch may creep
  into your shoes
  and steal your sleep
  by watching you.
So point your shoes
  away from the bed
  and she'll have to watch
  the wall instead.

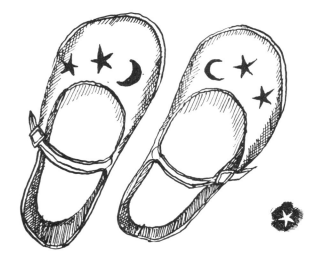

Please sit down 22

North American saying

If a stranger enters the house
They must sit down at least once.
If they don't, without a doubt,
They'll take your sleep when they go out.

Two pins crossed 23

Jamaican saying

Put two black pins crossed
  in a cotta of plantain cloth;
You'll sleep soon enough.

Make a bad dream go 24

A trick against nightmares, by Helen East

Steal a letter one at a time like this:

Bad dream go
ad dream go
d dream go
dream go
ream go
eam go
am go
m go
go
o
!

The neverending tale 25

North Indian story, retold by Nikhat Mohamed

Imagine it's a warm summer's night in Bangladesh. The whole family have taken their beds outside into the yard, open to the sky and the stars. The children don't want to go to sleep. They cuddle up to their nurse, their buwa, demanding stories. 'Tell us a very long story, Buwa. Tell us a story that never, never ends.'

'Alright,' she says, 'but you mustn't go to sleep in the middle of my story. You must hunkara. I shall ask if you are still awake and you must say "hnng:"'

'Are you ready?'
'Hnng.'
'Will you stay awake?'
'Hnng!'

'I'm not telling you what I have seen, I am telling you what I have heard. So any blessings or curses should fall on the shoulders of the real creator of the story.

'Once upon a time there was a Badishah, an emperor. He didn't have a son, but he had a beautiful daughter, Shahidzade. Tales of her beauty had spread far and wide, and princes from all over the world wanted to marry her, but the Badishah had still not chosen anyone.

Now the Badishah had everything he could wish for, but he had one problem: he could not sleep. He had tried everything – almond oil on his head, gentle massage of his legs, hot milk and poppy seed drinks at bedtime, but nothing worked. So at last he decided that whoever could make him sleep would win the princess and half the kingdom. His messengers went out with great drums to call the people and tell them the news:

"Khilqual-khuda.
Ki-mulk Badishah ka.
Suno sunney walo!"

(That means: The people are God's people. The kingdom is the King's kingdom. So everyone come and listen!)

"The Badishah has said that whoever makes him sleep will win the princess and half the kingdom. But if you try, and fail – then you will lose your life. You will be beheaded."

So everyone came and tried their best. But no-one could make the Badishah sleep. And so they lost their heads, one by one. Many princes and brave young men all died.

At last there came a man who was not a prince; he was not even rich. But he was tired of all the killing and bloodshed and he was determined to stop it. He came to the Badishah and said, "I will tell you a story and I will make you sleep. But you must promise me one thing. You must promise not to interrupt me, or leave, or stop listening until I have finished."

"I promise," said the Badishah. "And if I break my promise you may do to me as I would to you – you may cut off my head."

"Very well," said the man, and so he began:

"Once upon a time there was a King, and he had a very big kingdom. And this kingdom was green and rich; full of wheat and rice and fruit. But one day all the fortune tellers and gypsies who could see into the future, came to the King and said, 'Sire, we have seen signs and omens. There will be a great drought, and the rivers and wells will dry up, and all the crops will fail. And your people will die of hunger.'

And the King said, 'Very well. But I will beat this drought. My people will not starve.'

So he called all his builders and carpenters, and he made them build a great barn – a vast great storehouse.

'And make sure,' he said, 'that there are no holes or cracks in it.'

So that was done, and when it was ready, he called all the landowners and made them bring sacks of wheat, until the barn was full right up to the roof.

The following year, just as the fortune tellers had foreseen, there was a terrible drought. Not a drop of rain fell, and nothing would grow, and the earth grew dry as dust, and the soil blew away in the wind. The animals, and the birds and the cattle began to die with hunger, but the King was not worried. He knew he had enough grain to save the lives of all his people.

But one of the builders had made a tiny mistake, and there was a chink in the roof of the barn. It was so small – hardly big enough for a mouse – no-one even noticed it. You could hardly see it. But one day, a bird flying overhead saw that tiny hole. And she squeezed in through it and found all the grain in the barn. And so she went to all the other birds and told them, 'We can get our food here.'

So they started. One bird went into the barn and took one grain, and flew away. Then another went into the barn and took a grain and flew away."

The storyteller was saying it this way:

"Chirya aee dana lagai phur-say.
Chirya aee dana lagai phur-say."

(This means: Then another bird came and took a grain of corn and flew away.)

Now the Badishah, listening to the story, started to get bored. And because he was bored, he started yawning. And because he was yawning he started feeling sleepy . . . and sleepier . . . and sleepier.

"Are you still awake, Badishah?" said the storyteller.

"Hnng."

"Then another bird took a grain and flew away. *Chirya aee dana lagai phur-say . . .*"

And so it went on and on until at last the Badishah said, "Alright, alright, now stop that and get on with the story. What happened next?"

"But my Lord," said the storyteller, "the big barn is still full of grain and the sky is still dark with birds and they are still coming and taking one grain and flying away. *Chirya aee dana lagai phursay.*"

"But!" said the Badishah, "what happened after that?"

"My Lord," said the storyteller, "you must wait until the whole store is emptied, grain by grain, and all the birds are fed. Then I will tell you what happened next. But first the barn must be emptied grain by grain, and if you stop me – remember your promise. You will lose your head!"

So the Badishah had to listen on and on and on. Was he still awake?

"Hnngzzzz."

'Are you still awake, children?'

'Hnng.'

'Shut your eyes and see those birds – one by one by one. *Chirya aee dana lagai phursay.*'

'So the Badishah fell asleep at last and the storyteller won the princess and half the kingdom. All because the Badishah couldn't listen to any more birds coming to take a grain of corn. Can you?

Chirya aee dana lagai phursay.
Chirya aee dana lagai phursay.
Chirya aee dana lagai phursay.'

Counting sheep 26

Sleep trick from England

To make you sleep, try counting sheep going through a gap.
Trouble is they never go in a neat and tidy row.
Some push forwards, some sneak sideways,
   Some go doubling back.

Fuoch chi 'rioed yn morio? 27

Song from Wales sung by Mary Medlicott

'Fuoch chi 'rioed yn morio?'
'Wel, do, mewn padell ffrio;
    Chwythodd y gwynt
    fi i'r Eil o Man
A dyna lle bûm i'n crio!'

Where did you go to last night? Make up your own verses and travel on round the world. The Welsh words mean.

    'Have you ever been sailing?'
    'Yes, in a frying pan.
      The wind blew me
      to the Isle of Man
    And there I was a'crying.'

You can sing this song as a round – like London's burning. The second person (or group) starts singing when the first gets to the note marked ★ in the music.

Last night as I lay sleeping,
I dreamt that I was sailing
    To the Isle of Man
    in a frying pan,
And back again by morning.

Last night as I lay sleeping,
I dreamt that I was riding
    To the Isle of May
    on a seahorse sleigh,
And back again by morning.

Last night as I lay sleeping,
I dreamt that I was floating
    To the Isle of Dogs
    on a raft of logs,
And back again by morning.

Last night as I lay sleeping,
I dreamt that I was skiing
    To the Isle of Capri
    on a single ski,
And back again by morning.

Seven sleepers sleeping on 28

Sleep trick from Europe

Constantine, Serapion, Maximian, Malchus, John,
Dionysios, Marcian, Seven Sleepers sleeping on.
Name one twelve times soft and slow,
You'll be asleep before you know:
      Constantine, Constantine, Constantine, Constantine,
          Constantine, Conssss . . .

Disappearing trick 29

A song for banishing ghosts, by Helen East

Make up a sign or an action for each word. For instance, ghost in British sign language is:

Six ghosts lurking in the shadow of the door,
Six ghosts lurking in the shadow of the door,
But if one jumps out at me, at least I can be sure
There'll be one less ghostie in the shadow of the door.

Five ghosts lurking in the shadow of the _____

Four ghosts lurking in the shadow _____

Three ghosts lurking in the _____

Two ghosts lurking _____

One ghost _____

No _____

No _____
And if none jump out at me, at least I can be sure
There are no ghosts lurking in the shadow of the door.

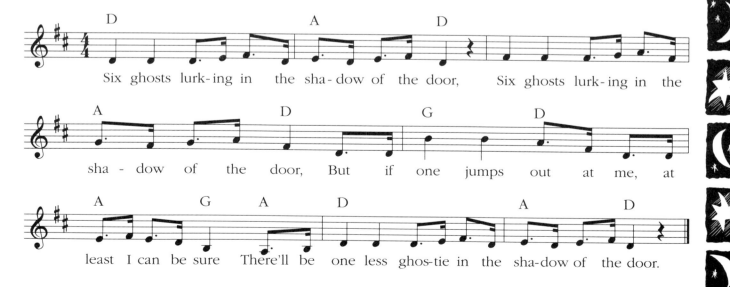

First light ㉚

Jewish story from Eastern Europe, retold by Pamela Marre

In the beginning, God created the Heaven and the Earth, and all was darkness. And God said: 'Let there be light.'

And there was light.

And God divided the light from the darkness. And God called the light Day, and the darkness he called Night. And the evening and the morning were the first day.

But God didn't create the sun and the moon until the fourth day, so where do you think the light came from that made the day different from the night?

Well, God ran his hand under the waters which covered the face of the whole earth. He ran his hand over the hard rock that lay underneath the continuous sea until he felt a knobble sticking up from the surface. He grasped it and pulled hard, and the rock rose up in his hand like dough, and the end he was holding tore loose and he held it in his fist. And where he had pulled at the face of the earth, he left a peak of rock standing with a broken top, which is now Mount Ararat.

Well, God opened his hand out flat so that the piece of rock that he had pulled from the earth sat on it, and then he breathed on the rock, and it absorbed his breath and became translucent and began to glow. And he breathed on it three times and after the third breath the rock was full of light and colours that danced, and then God laid the rock on the summit of Mount Ararat until the fourth day to light the world. And the rock glowed and pulsed and shimmered with all the colours of the rainbow. Can you imagine all those colours glowing in turn inside that magic rock?

Now close your eyes and see if you can see,
Try and imagine along with me.

Fill your mind with red – deep, dark and warm:

Red like the colour of my dressing gown;
All warm and woolly when you snuggle
  down
Deep into my arms for a night-time hug.
Then into your cot all cosy and snug.
  Goodnight room.

Now imagine orange, glowing:

The sky was orange at the end of today
When the sun gave out his very last ray.
He climbed down into his bed for the night
Then covered himself, and out went the light.
  Goodnight sun.

Can you see yellow now – pale moonlight

That gleams on toy parrot, who hangs in
  your room.
He flew from his home by the light of the
  moon.
He flew over deserts, he flew over seas,
To come and live with you for as long as
  you please.
  Goodnight parrot.

Let a wave of green roll over your eyes:

Now fill your mind with green woods and
  green trees,
Green dappled shadows and rustling leaves.
An owl gives a hoot that makes a mouse
  leap,
While deep in her burrow, rabbit's asleep.
  Goodnight rabbit.

Now the green is darkening, darkening . . .

Until it's become the deep blue of the sea,
And under the water the fish swim free.
They swim over rocks, they swim under
    whales
Who lazily sing their travellers' tales.
    Goodnight fish, goodnight whales.

And as we go deeper and deeper under the sea,
The blue gets darker and darker and darker
    until:

It's indigo – colour of the sky at night.
You may think it's black, but it isn't quite –
It's lit by the stars and the pale moonbeams,
Who may carry angels into your dreams.
    Goodnight, little one, sleep tight.
    Sweet dreams.

Ghoom-parani gaan ③1

Lullaby from Bangladesh, sung by Fahmida Monju Majid

Aey chand, amaar sathe khelbi jodi aey,
Amay nie jaare aji tor shonar naye.

'Oh Moon, would you come and play with me today?
Would you bring your golden boat and take me far away.'

A - ey chand,   a - maar   sa - the   khel - bi   jo - di   a - ey,
Oh   Moon,   would   you   come and   play with   me   to - day?

A - may   ni - e   jaa - re - a   ji   to - r   sho - nar naye.
Would you   bring your   gol - den boat and   take   me far a - way.

Good morning

As Folo says, this is a song for a rowdy street procession. Invent some lively percussion for it – we've used tin cans scraped together.

Rise at 6

Let the children make up a rhyme to fit their day.

Did you sleep well?

This rhyme is based on a Bohemian superstition which is also found in the Middle and Far East, i.e. avoid answering anything directly! This is also the basis for many children's playground repartee games, e.g.

Q.   What's your name?   A. Just the same
Q.   Where do you live?   A. Down the lane. etc.

This and the other sayings, charms and tricks (most of which I have rephrased to make them scan easily and stay in the memory) are all drawn from the superstitions and beliefs of many countries. The discovery of this type of material can extend into class and homework. It can be an interesting and entertaining entree into projects, e.g. try comparing beliefs for bringing good luck on special days: weddings, births, naming ceremonies, etc.

Snore snore snore

I wrote this story and cumulative chorus for this collection (it is dedicated to my mother and her menagerie). Other animals or visitors may be added or substituted as you like. Alternatively, instruments could be substituted for voices in the chorus to emphasize and extend its percussive potential.

Nu wahtan

Waking up can be a slow and peaceful affair with this song from the Gambia, and as teacher and storyteller, Marie Ngum, suggests, this may result in a happier and more relaxed child. Her song can be used as well to give children who are already awake a chance to start again and re-awaken in a more co-operative and communicative state.

In the Gambia, the song would be accompanied with a calabash, the sound of which is softened by resting it on a pillow, or bowl of water.

Waking the Mogul princess

The princess in question was actually the spoilt teenage granddaughter of the last Mogul emperor of India, Bahjadur Shah Zafar, who died in exile.

The maids stroked the princess's feet with a rosebud – a pleasant enough way to awaken anyone. Try it literally to waken a sleeping child, or as a game to test their sense of touch. The 'sleeping' child guesses what you are using to stroke their feet (a feather, a piece of velvet, a bunch of blossom).

Instead of telling the children the trick of the mirror at the end, let them try to guess what the maids did. Can they think of any other ways to wake someone gently from sleep?

Bad luck!

I based this poem on old English superstitions about what to avoid when starting the day. When Carol Sherman turned it into a rap she added a pinch of Jamaican dialect to the flavour.

Dr Knickerbocker

This playground game was taught to me by children of the Army Base School, Digby Theddar, Lincs. The leader can choose any rhythmic variation they want, and the others have to copy it. This is a good opportunity to develop and explore rhythm and linked movement.

El calentamiento

This game is for limbering up – and driving sleep from body and mind. The literal meaning of the words is:

This is the warm up game –
We'll have to see how the rider loads up.
Rider! Load up! One hand . . .

A la carga! is the army command to load up a rifle ready to fire. It has a symbolic meaning here, referring to the rider's own body needing to be charged up or made ready.

Jinete! A la carga! and the list of parts, should be called by a solo voice. The list can serve as a useful introduction to some basic Spanish vocabulary. Alternatively English or other languages can be used, depending on who is the caller. This role can be passed to another person for each new verse.

When Spanish is sung vowels are often elided. This happens on *este el*, which is sung *estel*, and *todo el*, sung *todel*.

The golden bridge

The opening (*Riddle me red or guess me grey, show me who's jag or sajag today*) draws on the difference between being physically awake – jag (like red: live, burning, physically powerful), and mentally awake – sajag (like grey: thoughtful, meditative, absorbed). The words, jag and sajag, are Gujerati, and are used here because they express simultaneously the similarity and the difference between the two states in a way no English expression can match.

The solution to the (dreamer's) dilemma is to wake up. Don't give it away at once though – first, let the children explore their ingenuity and inclination for adventure – a well tried and sucessful method of promoting story-making.

Skunny Wundy's skipping stone

This is a Seneca tale, which storyteller, writer and poet, Joseph Bruchac (himself of Abenaki descent) heard as a child. This and other Skunny Wundy (meaning 'cross the creek') stories he now tells to his own children – so pass it on, as he does.

Dummy dance

This dance and accompanying percussion was taught to Rick Wilson by Getano Bann, a musician and poet, and Torres Straits aboriginal of Australia.

When Polynesian and Melanesian people came to Australia two thousand years ago, they introduced certain seated dances and drums into the existing culture. This particular social dance 'Sĕpsegul' (the dummy dance) is so called because it contains no actual words.

A Highland lullaby

This well-known Highland lullaby tells of a child stolen away forever by the fairies. The lullaby could therefore lead into work on enchantments, or visits to and from other worlds. Feelings of loss so hauntingly conveyed here by the music and imagery, might also be explored.

The King's storyteller

Duncan Williamson is a Scottish traveller, and this is just one of the thousands of traditional stories and ballads passed on to him from family and friends. This particular story is not necessarily rooted in Scotland – the kingdom mentioned 'could be anywhere', and variants of this story can be found in America and Europe. In a classroom, the idea of competing to be the king's storyteller suggests opportunities for drama and role playing, which may add an edge to the children's own storytelling.